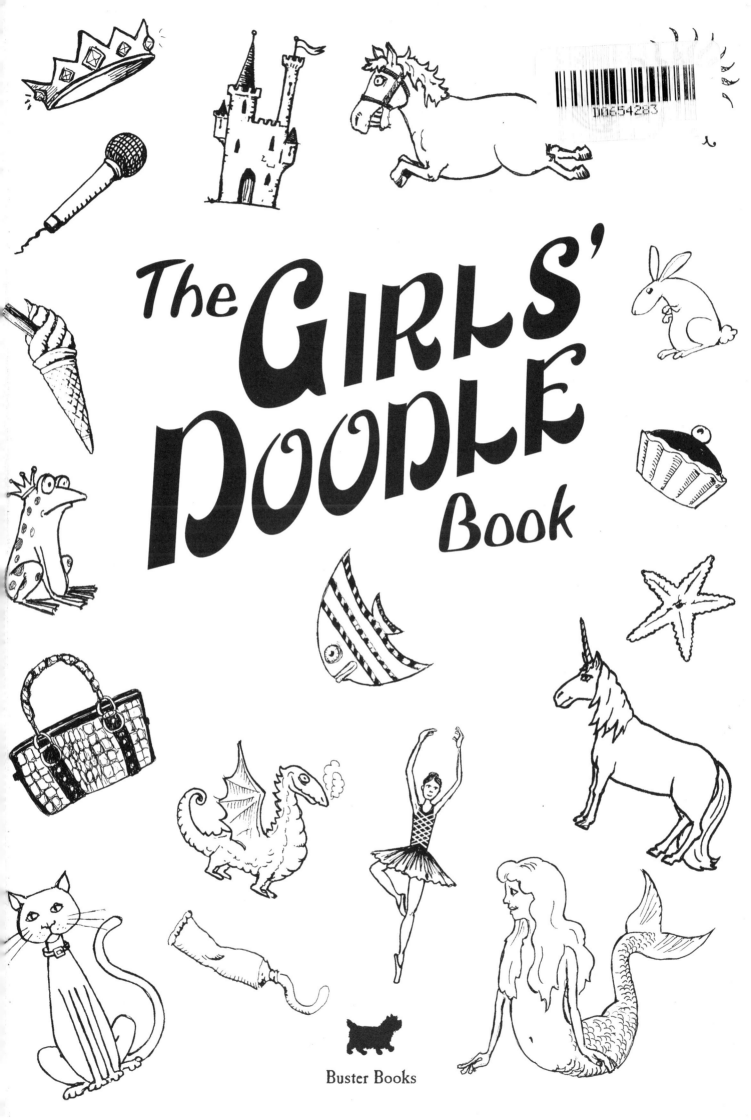

The GIRLS' DOODLE Book

Buster Books

Illustrated by Andrew Pinder

First published in Great Britain in 2008 by Buster Books,
an imprint of Michael O'Mara Books Limited,
9 Lion Yard, Tremadoc Road,
London SW4 7NQ

A CIP catalogue record for this book is available from the British Library.

ISBN: 978-1-906082-22-2

6 8 10 9 7 5

Printed and bound in Finland by WS Bookwell, Juva

www.mombooks.com/busterbooks

Draw the best bouquet.

Give the fish a fabulous home.

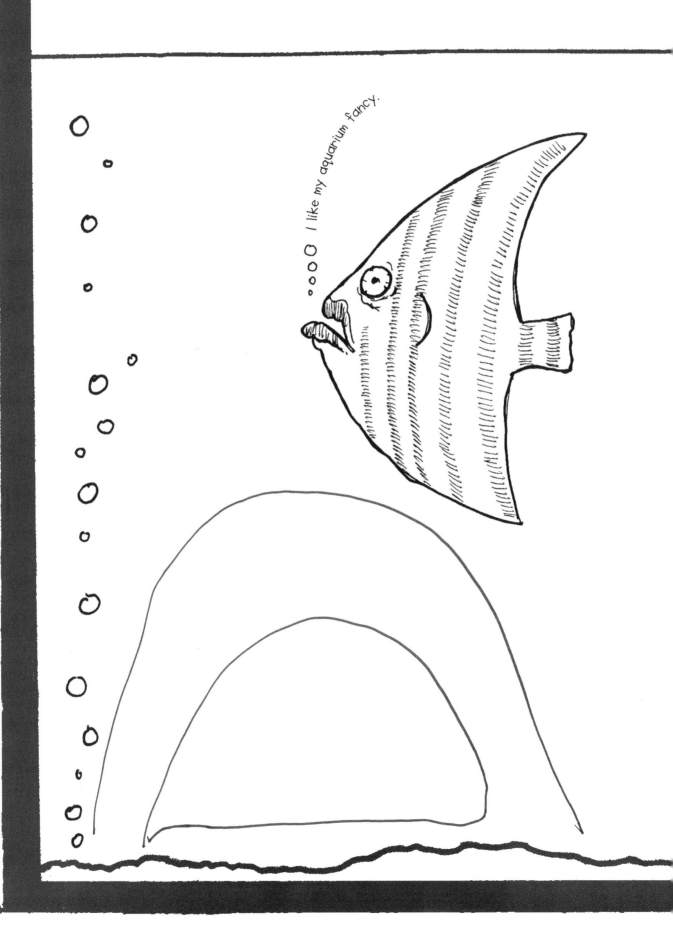

Populate the penguin colony.

Will I grow up to be like you?

Create your perfect party cake.

Draw each dog a designer outfit.

You look ruff.

Fill the hamsters' cage with fun.

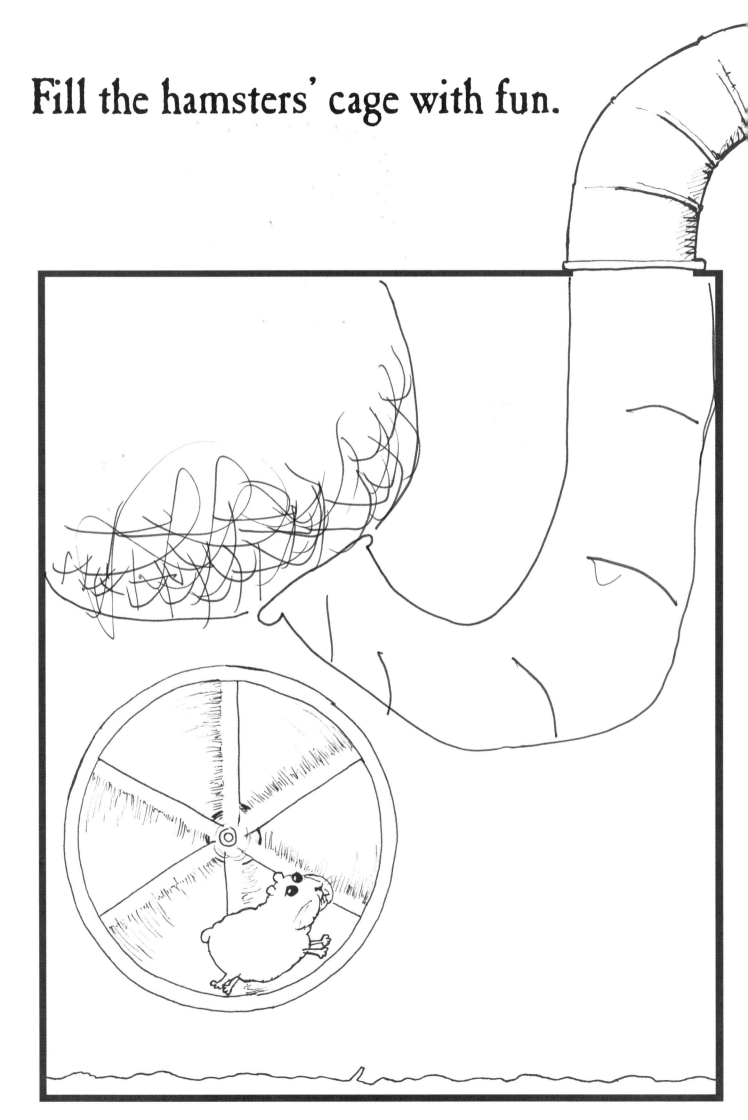

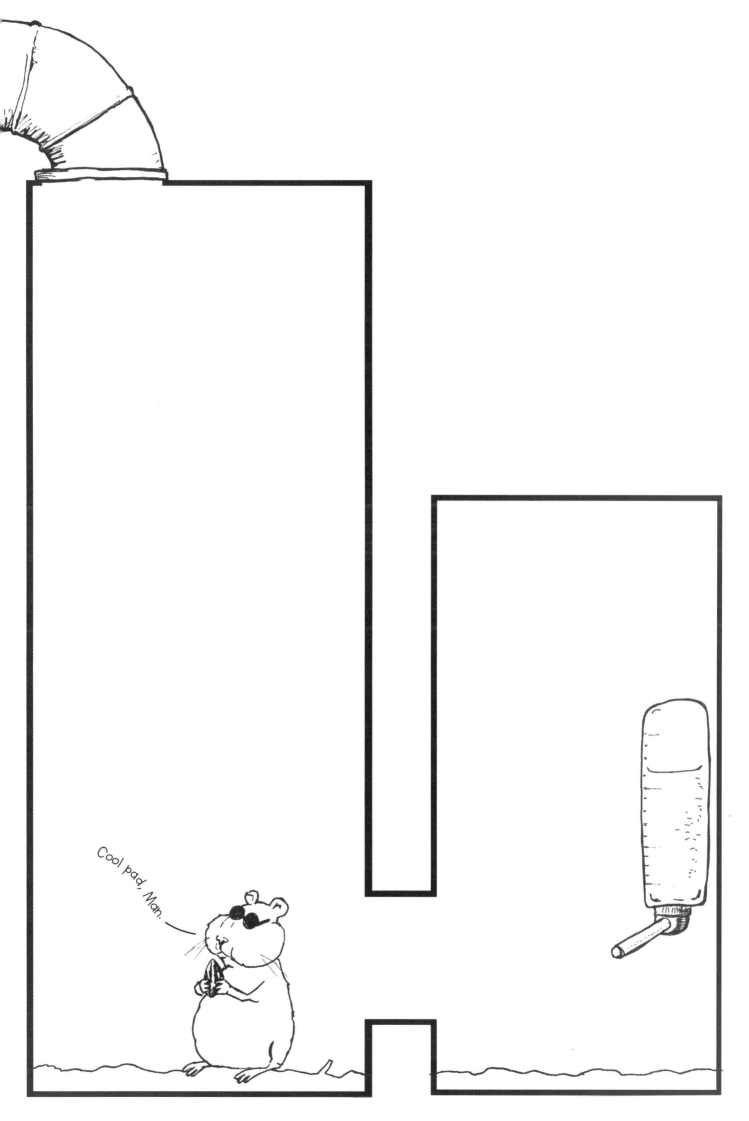

Give Mademoiselle big hair.

Add a pal for the parrot.

I need someone to squawk to.

Where are the fairies hiding?

Coming, ready or not.

What is Coco juggling?

Oh, no! What has Gran knitted now?

Fill the pond with lilies.

Decorate her hands with henna.

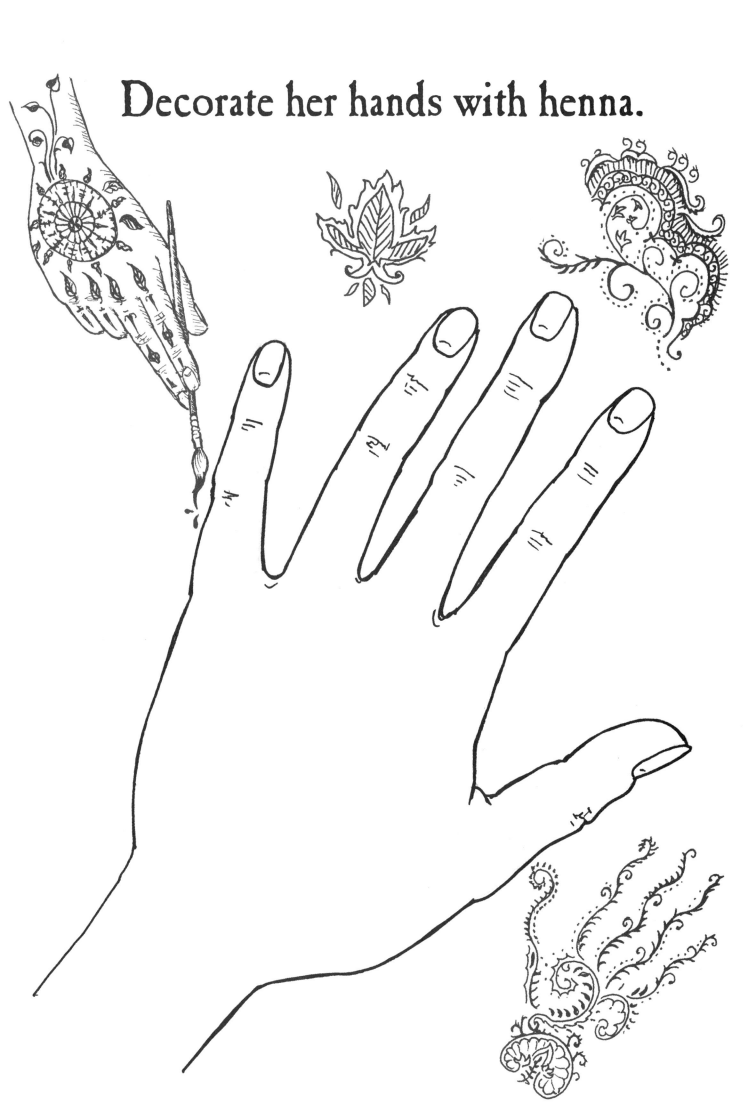

What do you see in the crystal ball?

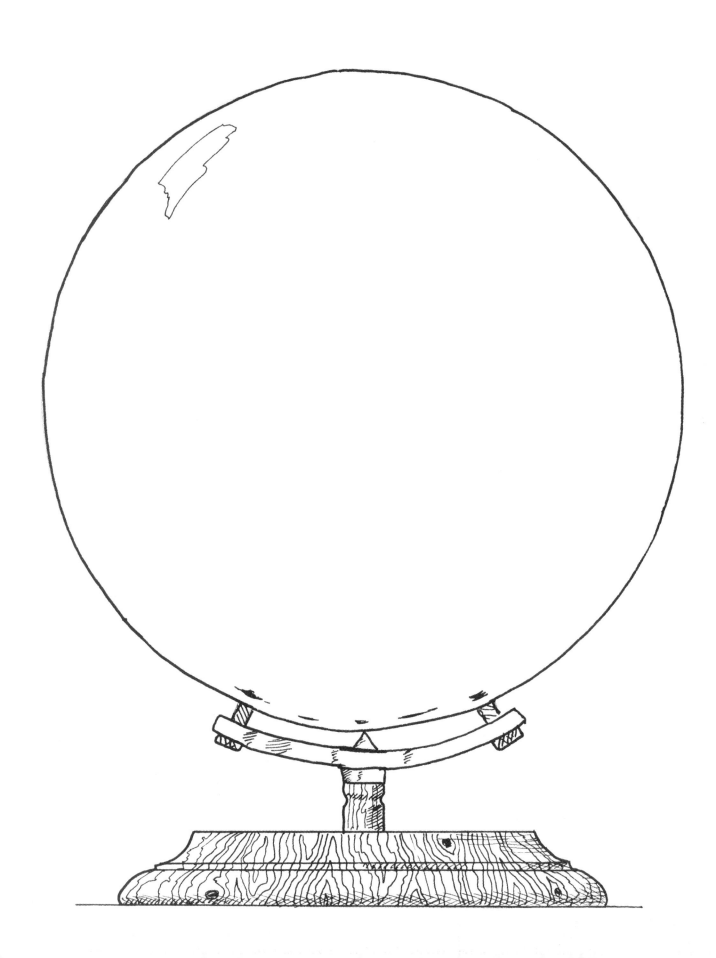

Shower the diva with flowers.

Imagine a mermaid's treasure.

It's mine, all mine.

Design the world's coolest phone.

My phone's got wi-fi, bluetooth, MP3, GPS, video, a camera, SMS. It's hands-free and bakes cakes.

What has she built on the beach?

Who is in the burrow?

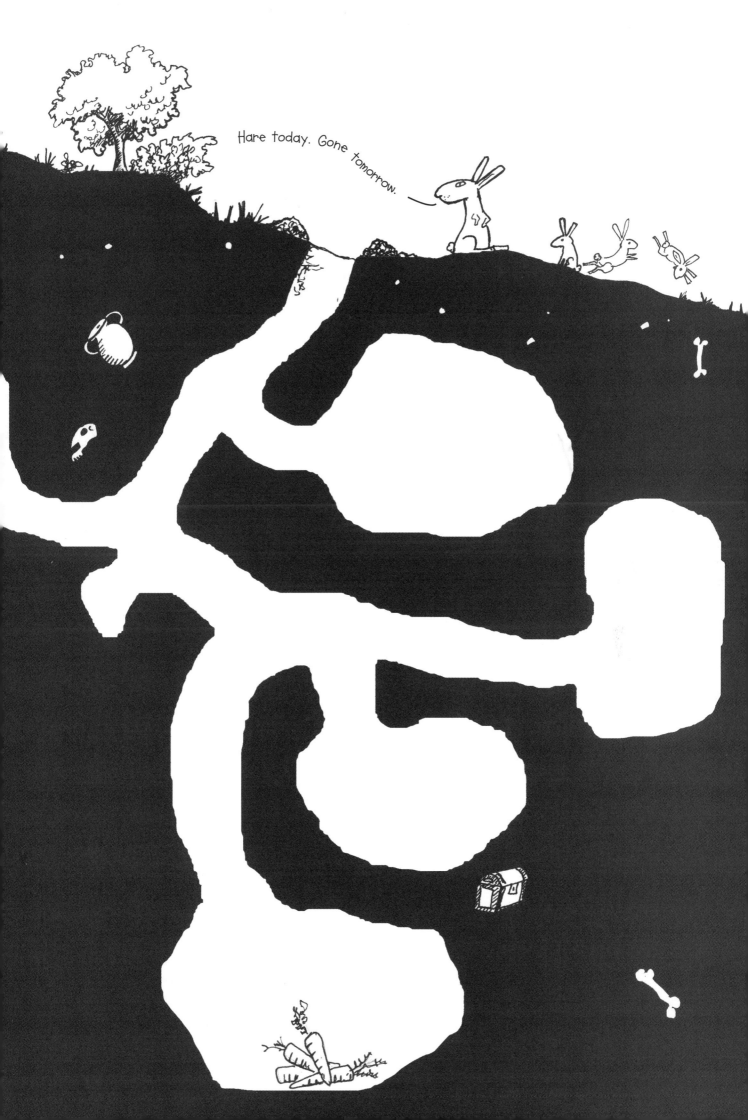

What are the dogs chasing?

Say cheese!

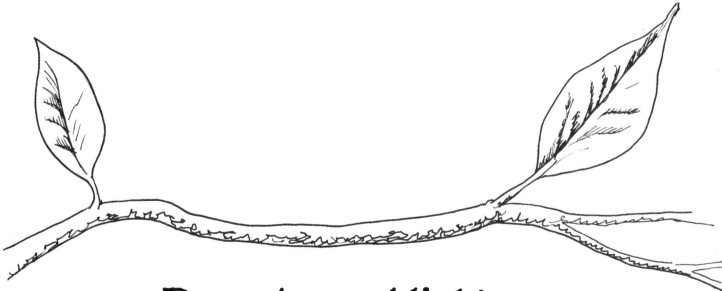

Draw the world's biggest and rarest butterfly.

What is she balancing on?

Design her super-costume . . .
. . . and one for the cat.

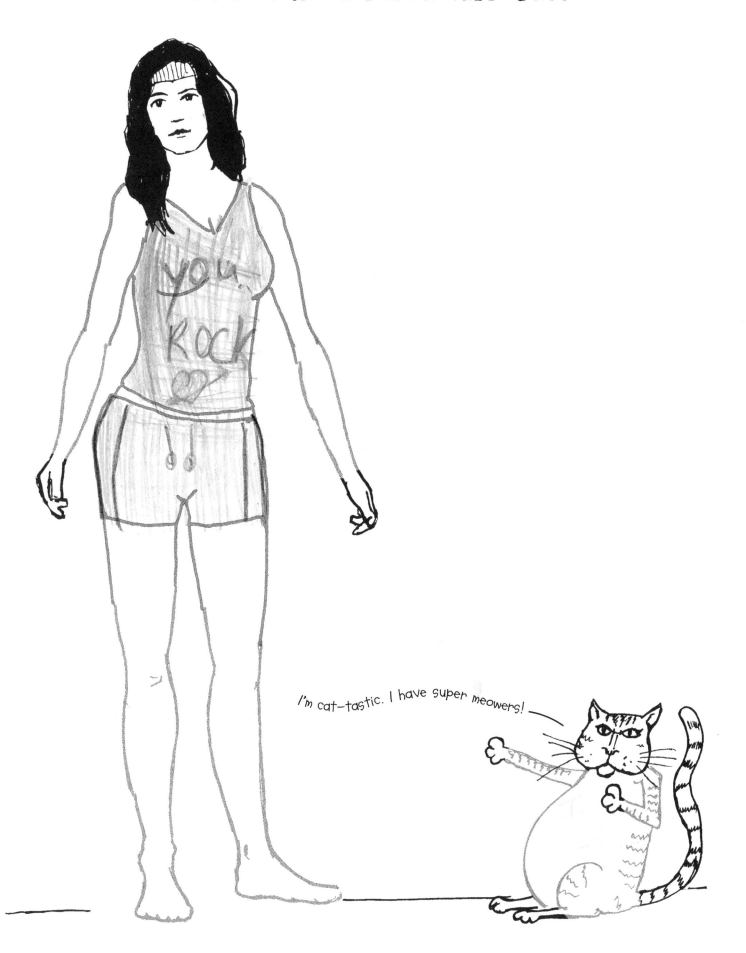

Design a CD cover and a T-shirt for her band.

Can you complete the roundabout?

Faster, faster.

Draw Bo Peep's sheep.

Don't tell me you lost them again!

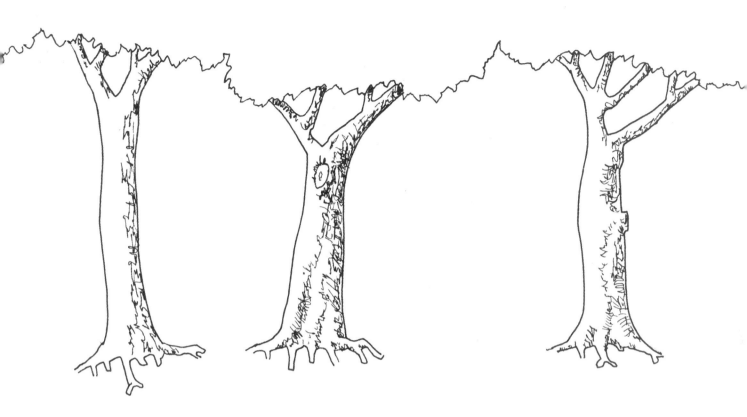

Draw a leaping dolphin.

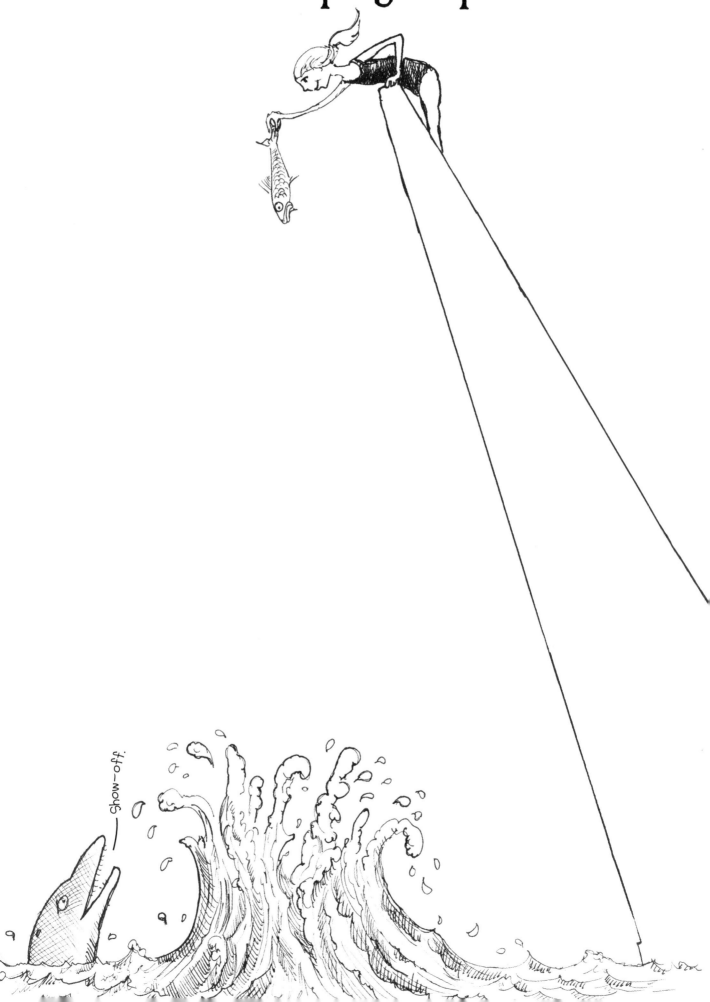

Show-off.

Beads and braids.

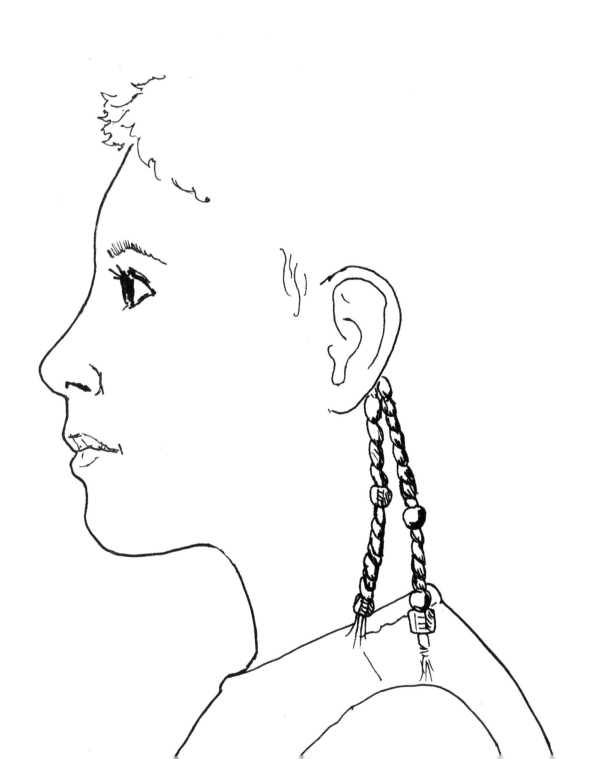

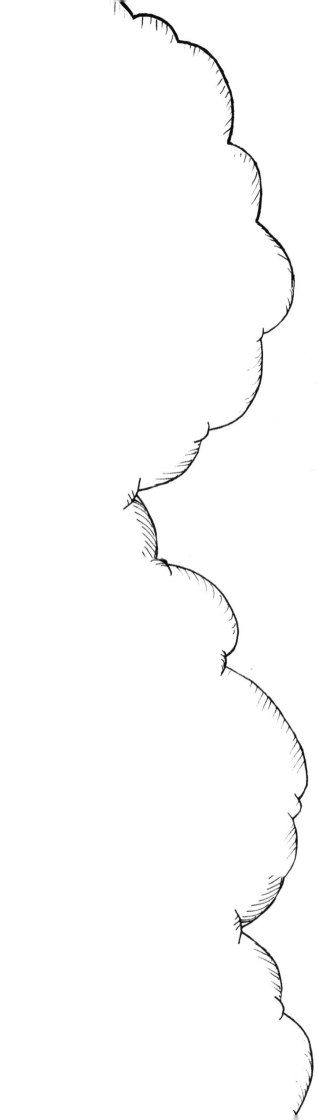

Design a fancy dress costume.

How will you save the kitten?

Who is balancing on the beam?

Decorate the box with shells.

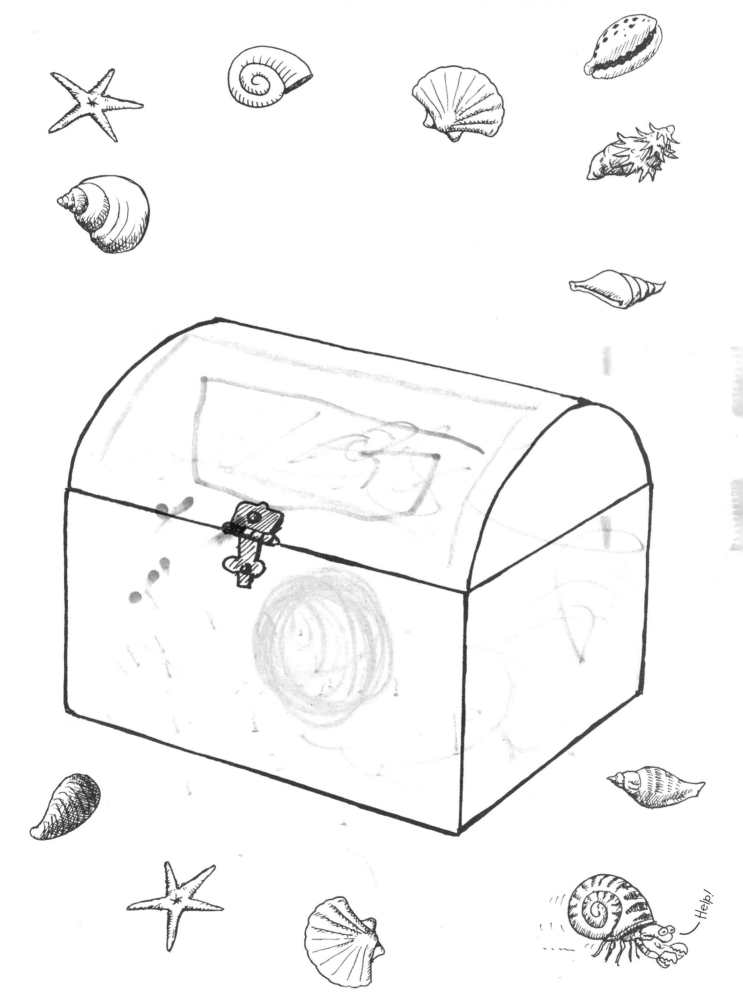

Help!

Paint their faces,
fans, and kimonos.

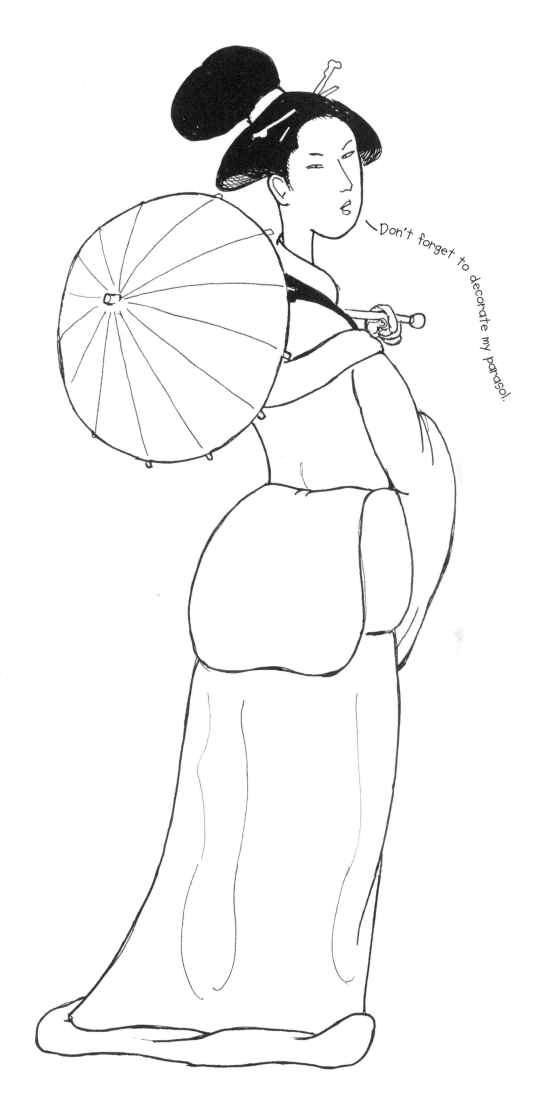

Put on a puppet show.

What is in her magic potion?

What will the frog turn into?

Who laid these eggs?

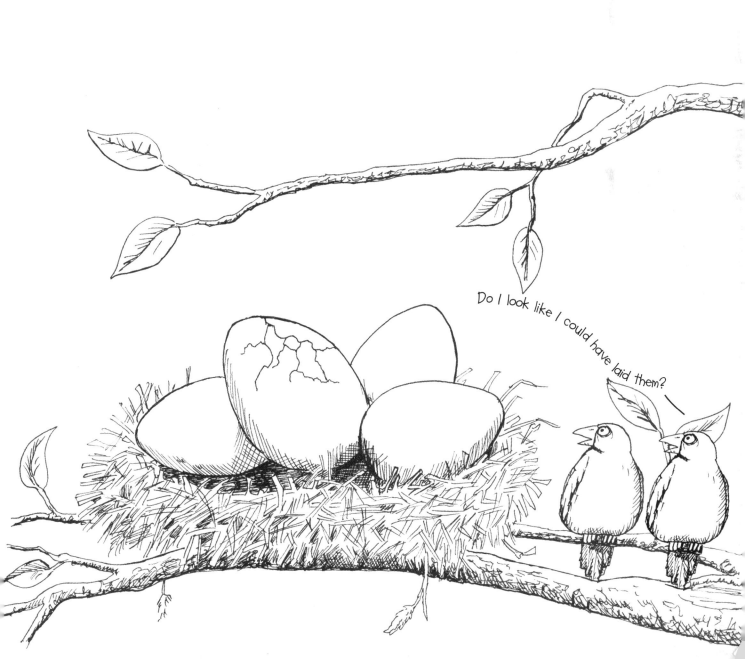

Finish building these igloos.

Picture a beach paradise.

Aloha!

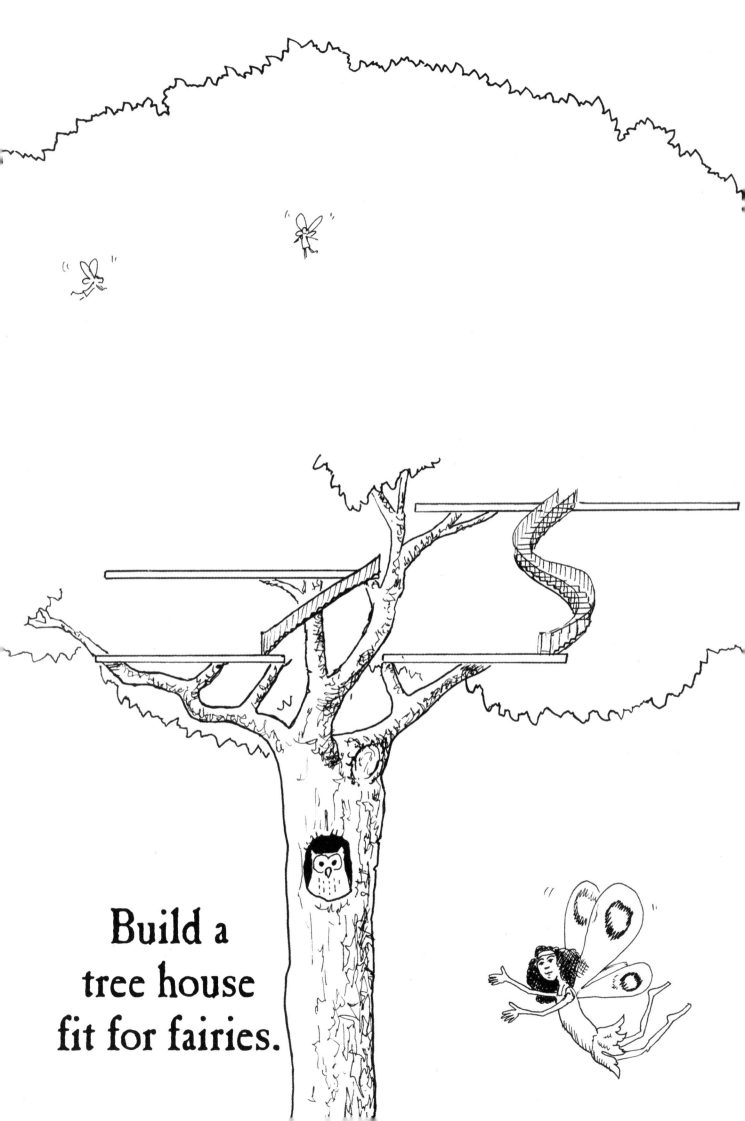

Build a
tree house
fit for fairies.

Can you finish the maze?

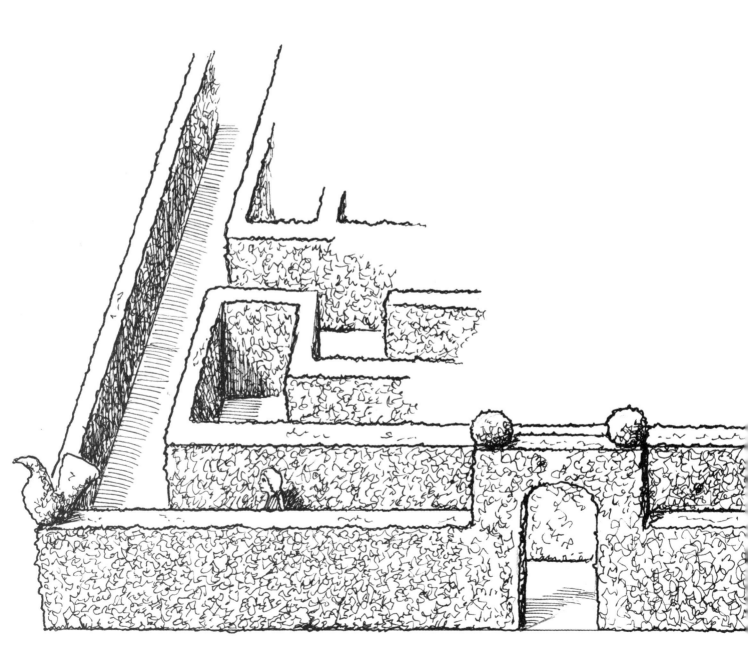

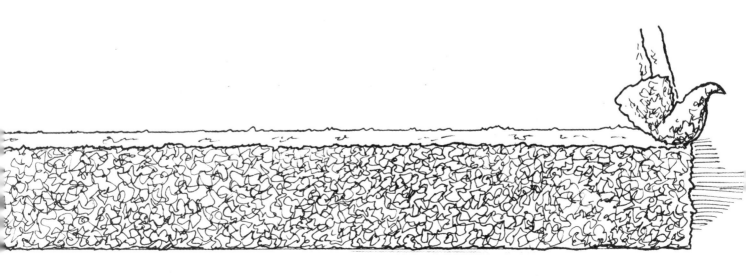

Decorate their teepees.

What would you take to a desert island?

Welcome to Tortoise Island.

Finish the helter-skelter.

The smaller the better.

Draw some
miniature masterpieces.

What can they see on the ghost train?

Decorate their saris . . .

. . . but don't forget the elephant's coat.

When it is complete make a wish.

Finish the daisy chain.

Design the
world's most
valuable tiara.

Make the sunflowers grow.

Complete this comic strip.

Put a tail on the bird of paradise.

I think that would really suit me.

What can they see in this Winter Wonderland?

What is in your sandwich?

Leave some cheese for me.

What is passing the café?

Such a beautiful bride!

What happened to her homework?

I can explain!!!

Okay

The primminister came to my house and
said Im doing a homework compertishon.
So he took my homework book. The
next week he came back and said
my pet cat Lion tued it up and he gave
me the tued peacess.

GRRRRR....

What is on at the movies?

Shhhhh!

Who is driving the car?

Design the cheerleaders' outfits.

Finish the gingerbread house.

What is in the secret garden?

A feast fit for a king.

PET SHOP

Draw the kittens in the shop.

How many butterflies?

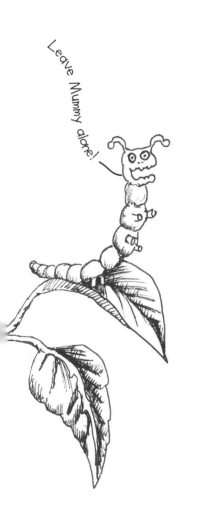

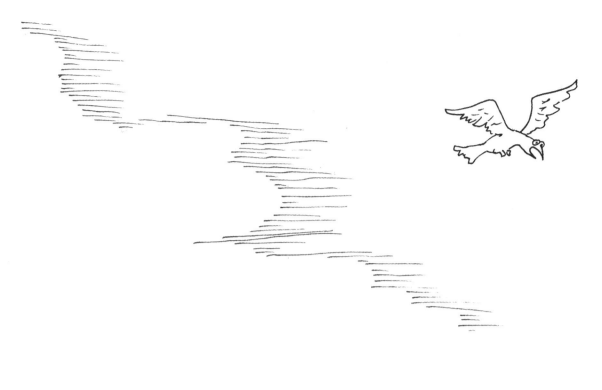

Where is she landing?

Twirl her ribbon.

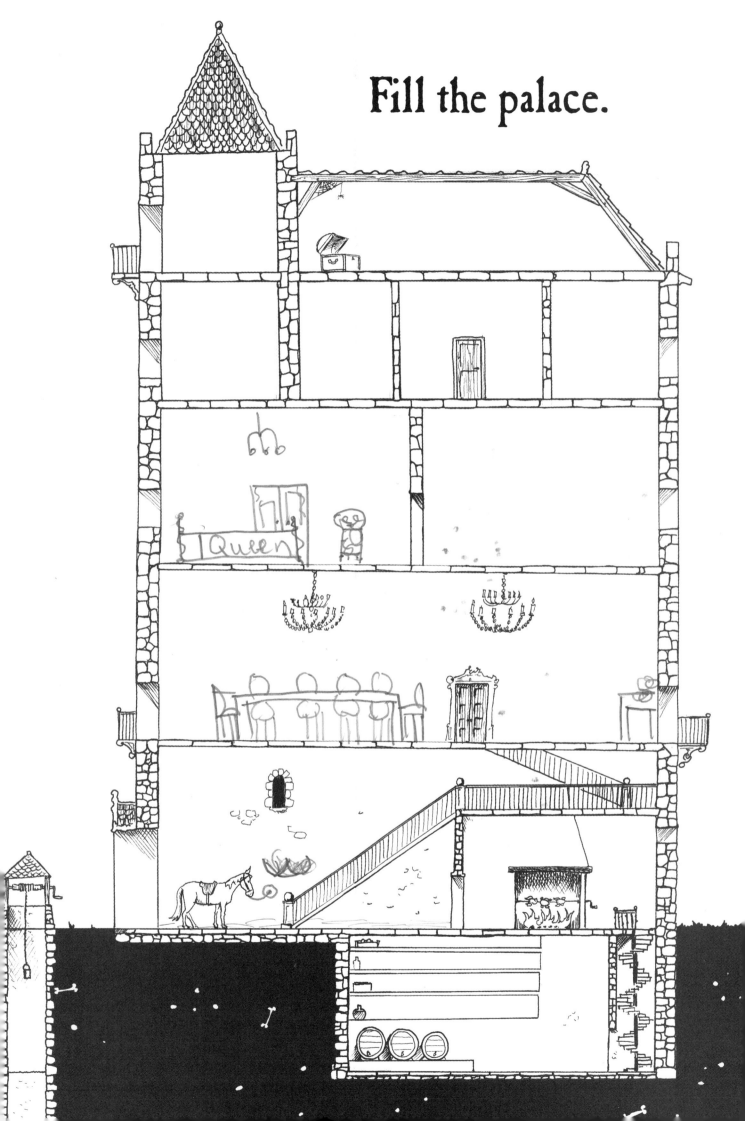

Fill the palace.

What is below the balloon?

Yummy!

Who is sailing the yacht?

Show a spectacular dive.

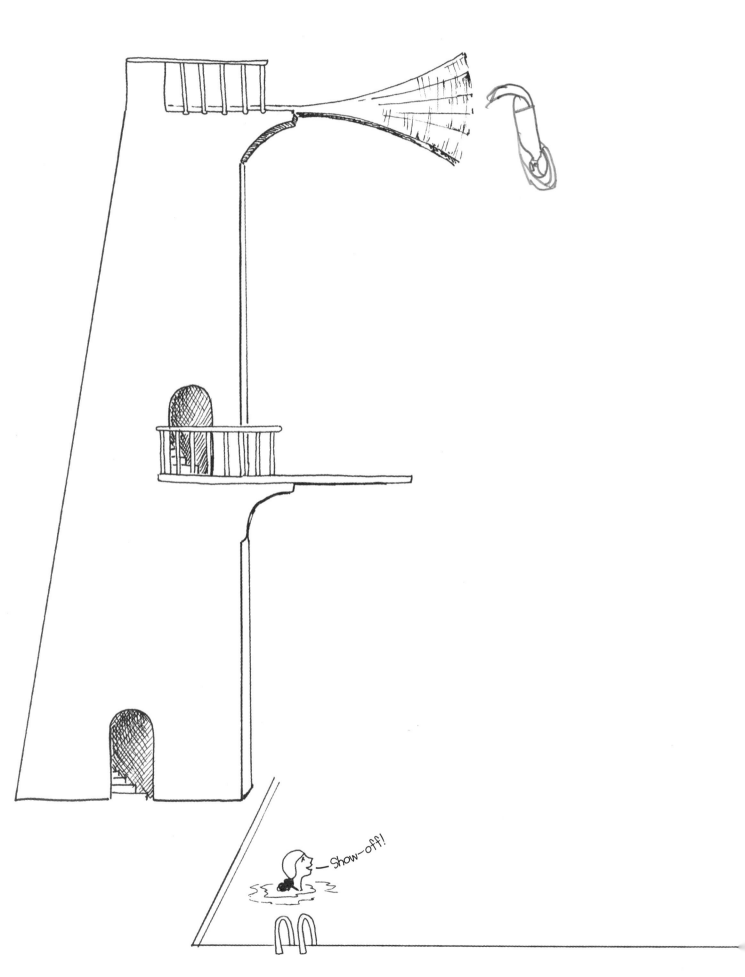

—Show-off!

Build the world's biggest snowman.

Design a completely new pet.

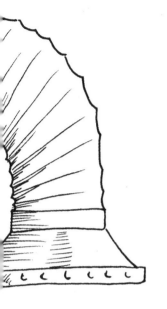

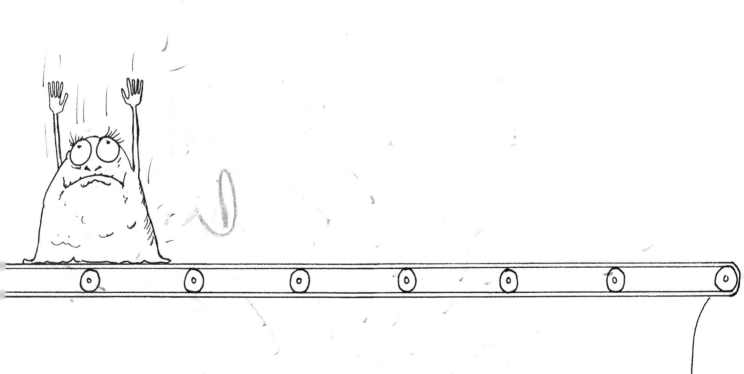

Who are they following?

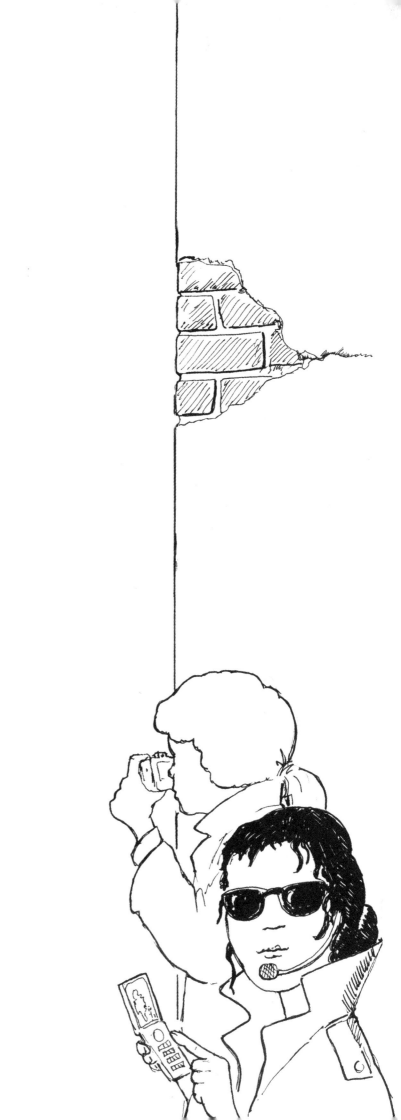

Who is sitting in the swingboats?

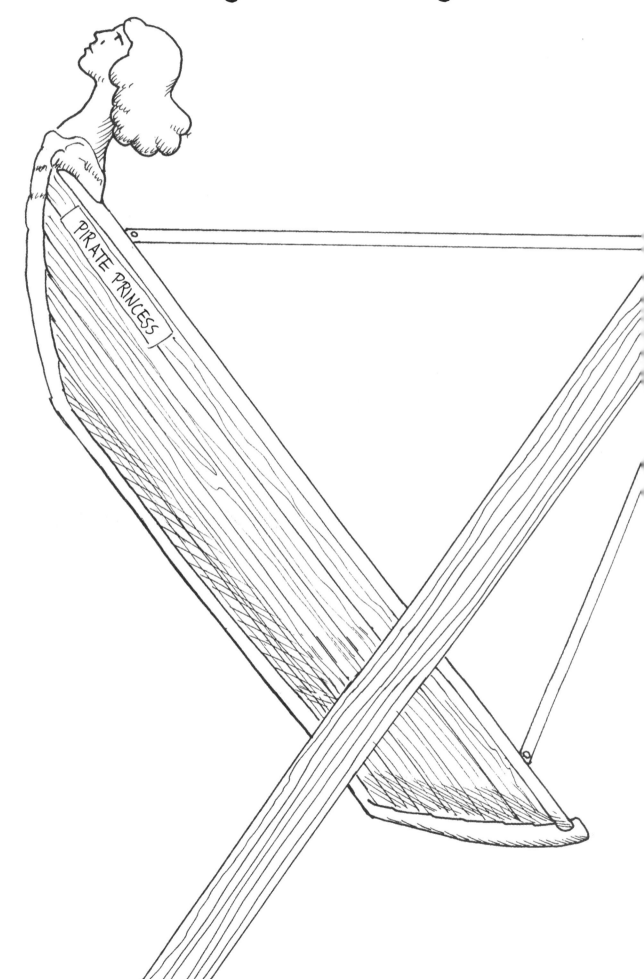

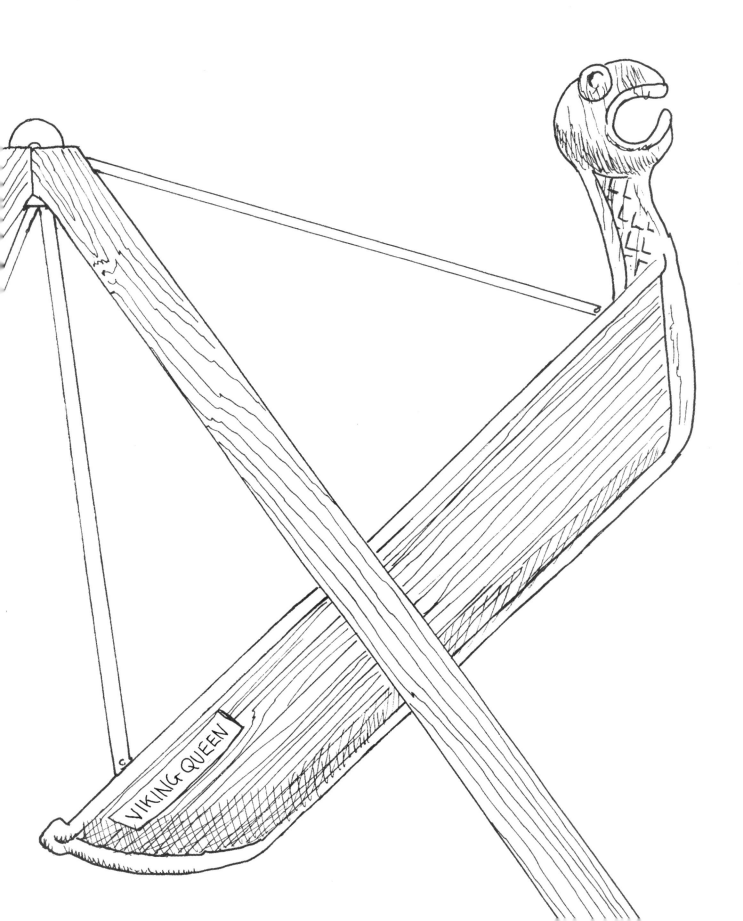

What has escaped from the zoo?

They went that way. Honest.

Who's kicking up the leaves?

Relax!

What is the princess sleeping on?

Who is crossing the rope bridge?

Fill the trees with woodland creatures.

Who is sitting around the campfire?

Fill the shelves with toys.

Put Cleopatra on her throne.

How will she get down?

Windsurfer girls.

Fill the sweetie jars . . .

... and the chocolate boxes.

Complete the street.

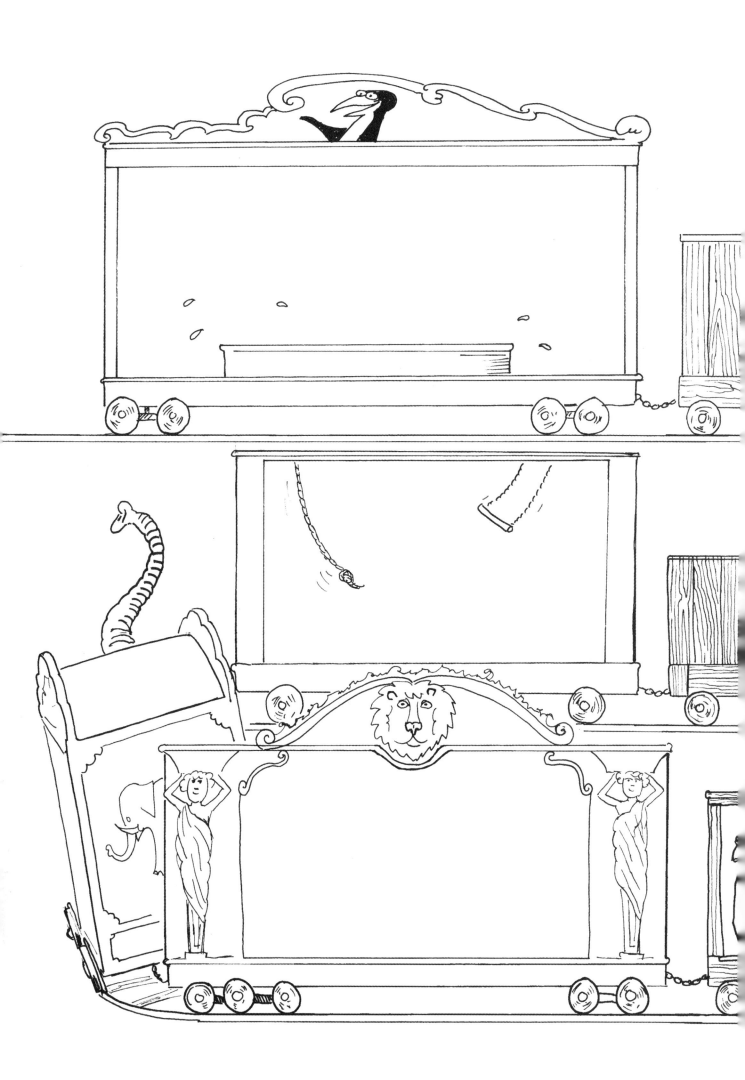

Who is coming to town with the circus?

Roll up. Roll up!

Decorate the beach hut.

What have the three little pigs built now?

What an enormous bunch of flowers!

How has he decorated the cake?

What has washed up on the beach?

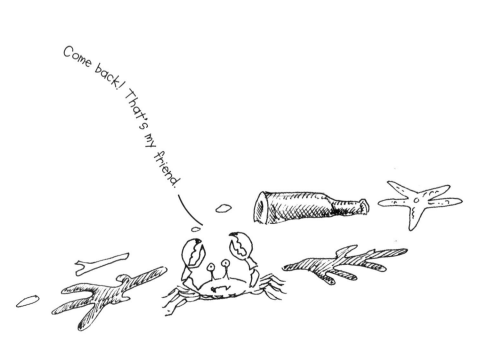

Help her paint the caravan.

Who is floating up, up and away?

What has the baby built?

Design your own really cool chess set.

King

Queen

Bishop

Put the finishing touches on the cuckoo clock.

Nice frame, not sure about the picture.

What an amazing painting!

Which pooches are prize-winning pets?

FATTEST DOG

BEST DOG

BEST HAIRCUT

SMALLEST
DOG

Oh no, man-eating plants. Run!

Who's travelling on the Egyptian barge?

Who is the fairest of them all?

Fill the pool with toys.

Mouse invasion!

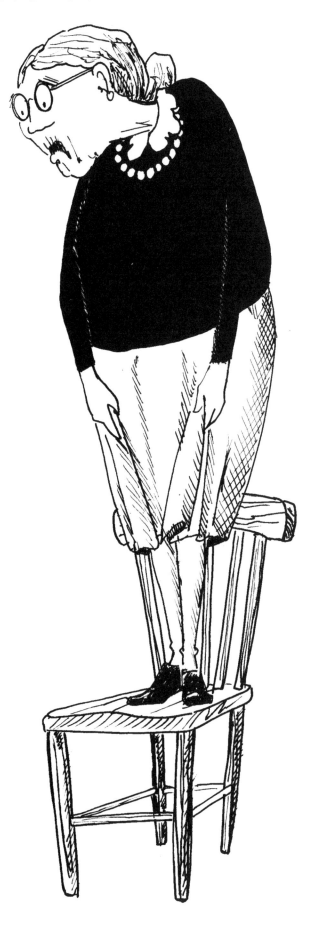

Who is making the baby cry?

Draw the spy-girl's secret weapon.

Doodle everyone a tail.

Mine is the waggiest.

Mine is the fluffiest.

Mine is the bushiest.

Mine is all tail.

Mine is the most beautiful.

Mine is the thinnest.

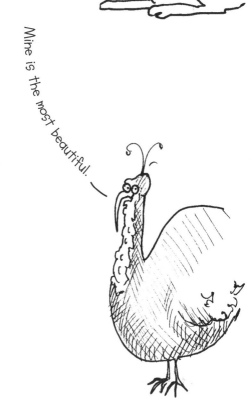

Mine is the flattest.

Mine is the curliest.

Mine is the most useful.

Mine is the scariest.

What can she see with her extraordinary X-ray specs?

The world's only dancing-tortoise troupe.

Look at them go!

What will you wish for at the wishing well?

What is in the trolley at the toy shop?